1 is One

By

TASHA TUDOR

Rand McNally & Company   Chicago • New York • San Francisco

© Henry Z. Walck, Inc., 1956
Standard Book Number: 8098-1047-6
Library of Congress Catalog Card Number: 56-11381
Printed in the United States of America

To Patricia Cummings

1 is one duckling

swimming in a dish

2 is two sisters

making a wish

3 is three swallows

up in the sky

4 is four sheep

nibbling rye

5 is five eggs

in a pretty round nest

6 is six children

all dressed in their best

7 is seven apples

on a little apple tree

8 is eight daffodils

you are picking for me

9 is nine red cherries

on a white china plate

10 is ten numbers

Tom has written on his slate

11 is eleven girls

dancing in a ring

12 is twelve baby birds

learning how to sing

13 is thirteen candles

upon a birthday cake

14 is fourteen mallard ducks

swimming on a lake

15 is fifteen roses

being made into a wreath

16 is sixteen rabbits

playing on a heath

17 is seventeen gourds

hanging up to dry

18 is eighteen stars

twinkling in the sky

19 is nineteen flowers

that little Jane has drawn

20 is twenty geese

flying toward the dawn

A IS FOR ANNABELLE

By Tasha Tudor

"A is for Annabelle, Grand-mother's doll..." in this charmingly illustrated alphabet book. Two little girls play with the elegant, old-fashioned doll, whose clothes and possessions complete the alphabet. Annabelle's varied wardrobe, her dresses and fan, her slippers and veil, will please all little girls, as well as Tasha Tudor fans.

The simple verse and delicate drawings are Tasha Tudor at her best. Young readers will find this a memorable introduction to the alphabet and all those who love dolls will love Annabelle.

DATE DUE

WITHDRAWN

E J
Tud   Tudor, Tasha
        1 is one